DUNES REVIEW

MICHIGAN WRITERS COOPERATIVE PRESS

Michigan Writers
P.O. Box 2355
Traverse City, Michigan 49685
dunesreview@michwriters.org

ISBN 978-1-950744-05-3

Printed and bound in the United States of America.

Our cover art, "Blue," comes from a series of oil paintings entitled "Tree Series" by Lisa Schulte. She writes: "Painting is a prehistoric means of communication and my intention when painting is to capture an image that only I have seen and make it available for everyone. I enjoy carefully mixing and manipulating color and texture with bold brushstrokes to produce an image that is both pleasing and entertaining."

(Image courtesy of the artist)

DUNES REVIEW

Volume 24 Issue 1
Spring 2020

CONTENTS

WITH THANKS TO

OUR GENEROUS PATRONS

John Flesher
Susan Odgers
Anne-Marie Oomen
Nancy Parshall
Holly Wren Spaulding of *Poetry Forge*

Editors' Notes

There is a quality of suspension in many of the pieces in this issue that speaks to our times. Whether it's a washed-up hockey goon noticing the lake's silent and continuous upheaval, a mother witnessing her child's first step, or a transgendered speaker writing into the ongoing discomfort in their family—this writing takes note of the moment before definition or resolution. The "...end of something or everything / is, as ever, nigh, " writes Jeremy Gregersen. We remember and anticipate loss, snip a lock of hair to remember a loved one, or imagine the regeneration resulting from the death of baby foxes—losses we can only imagine. Roots keep appearing in this issue, as do visions of a world that keeps moving. Meanwhile, as Blake Lynch writes, we lie "awake / in our beds, like children waiting for something." Change is just around the corner. No, wait: it's already here. And as always, when reading what writers craft with such care, I find myself in good company. Thank you, contributors and readers, for joining us.

— Teresa Scollon

I really wish Bruce Springsteen had topped the charts in 1972. I wasn't around yet then, but it really would have made for a magical tie-in with yet another poem in this issue. We've got rock and roll, birds, roller derby, art galleries on country roads, and somehow a few threads manage to weave them all together, inviting us to arrange them in just the right sequence so that you, dear reader, may be pulled gracefully through this little book piece by piece.

"Something is happening again that has always happened and will keep on happening forever," says Paul Luikart, and it's true with every iteration of *Dunes Review* (if I may be so bold as to believe our little project will exist in perpetuity): the words of disparate contributors show up to be braided together, creating a new whole, even as they shine on their respective pages. The impermeable reflective greatness of a rainstorm or a Lake appears just over the next rise. We stand on shore, listen to the waves turn into each other moment by moment, find ourselves in the current.

—Jennifer Yeatts

Joe Davies

PUBLIC GALLERY

It was not satisfying. This was Nola's opinion, and Nola was Carl and Roberta's daughter, so one thing she was bound to have was opinions. Not always poor. However, in the case of this particular Emmental it came down to a simple case of taste, or lack of it. The flavour was bland, almost non-existent. This was what Nola said. She stood back, looking at the painting of the angular buildings covered in snow, which was now leaning against the base of the tree and said, "It looks great," meaning the painting, "but, really, didn't we bring any other cheese?"

"There's some Gouda," said Natalie, Nola's junior by a year. "But you won't like it either if you don't like the Emmental."

"What is it with this family and cheese? Can't anyone buy cheese with a little bite to it?"

"Well, everyone?" said Roberta, changing the subject. "Shall we move on? Nola, dear, there's some extra old cheddar somewhere near the bottom. I put it in first, but why don't you wait and we'll spread everything out at the next stop?"

"All right," said Nola, grudgingly.

"I like it," said Carl, still staring at the painting. His youngest daughter Mary, youngest of the three, stood at his side saying nothing. There was something loyal about her attitude, the way she stuck by him, voicing none of the passionate objections she'd given earlier. Here she was, dressed almost conservatively in a cotton print dress, the wind blowing just enough that she needed to hold her sun-hat, saying not a word against anything.

Without looking, Carl reached out and took Mary's free hand in his and gave it a squeeze. She returned it at once and just as firmly.

"It's good, Carl," said Roberta, "It's a good place for it, but how about we move on?"

"Yes," said Carl, "Next," and he wheeled abruptly and set off for the car.

"Someone want to help with the cooler?" said Nola.

"You're the one who dragged it out," said Natalie.

"Help her," said Roberta, and Natalie did.

A minute later, dust hung in the air, marking the spot where their car had been.

"There!" said Nola, pointing at a greying split rail fence, set among a tumble of stones and partially entwined by the thin old sticks of some expired hedge.

Carl slowed the car.

"It's not the best spot to spread out the food, but there is certainly something about it," said Roberta.

"I can wait," said Nola.

Natalie shot her a look, as if to say, "Oh, sure you can."

For a minute all five of them, mother, father, three daughters, all five looked at the fence, until finally Carl put the car in park and turned off the ignition. One by one the doors opened and out they stepped. Then, wading through knee-length grass, they approached the fence. It was quite beautifully situated. The tall grass, the stones, and on the other side, a broad and slanted field, curving up and off to the northeast, and filled entirely with some squat plant, bearing pale, iridescent, mustard-yellow flowers. The air was warm and moist and fragrant, almost tropical.

"I know just the one," said Carl, and he returned to the car and opened the trunk.

He came back carrying what looked to be a half-finished painting of a woman, in some ways little more than a sketch or suggestion. She stood in profile, naked to the waist, and seemed to be glancing back towards the viewer as if to say, "Come, follow me."

Once Carl had leaned it against the fence, Nola said, "You'd never have a painting of a man looking at you like that." It sat crookedly but was left as it was.

"What if it were painted by a woman?" said Natalie after a pause. "Would you feel differently?"

"What? Do you mean if this exact painting were painted by a woman, how would I feel?"

"I guess."

"Would a woman even paint another woman to look like that?"

"Girls," said their mother, "I don't think we need to talk about this right now, do we?" and she gestured with her head towards their father, as if to say, "Please, think of him."

This quieted them.

"Look," said Mary, softly, and pointed across the field to a line of trees. There stood three deer.

"Now this," whispered Nola, "is what I'd call a movie moment."

Natalie turned to look at her. "Really?" she said, keeping her voice low. "And what movie would that be?"

"Girls. Not now."

"I'm going to the car," said Nola.

"Not feeling well?"

"I've felt better."

"Okay, everyone," said Carl. "One last look."

Even Nola stopped and shot a glance over her shoulder. Uncannily, it was the same pose as in the painting.

A minute later they were on their way again, Nola with her hand in the cooler, looking for something to put in her mouth. Natalie saying, "Try the grapes. They're good ones." And Nola did.

"All I'm saying," said Roberta, "is I'd like to see someone walk up our front steps and try to tell me what my own home should look like. Whether I cut the grass or make a fence out of found objects or paint my front porch to look like the tunnel of love, what business is it of anyone else's?"

"It has to do with property values," said Carl.

"It's not just that," retorted Roberta. "It's the outward expression of some as yet undiscovered conformity gene. I'm sure of it. Be like us or go off and start your own herd. As if survival depended on everyone having their garage door painted from the same sickly palette."

"Well, thank goodness it wasn't us who got the letter."

"I'd tear it up. No, I'd photocopy it a hundred and fifty times in different shades of red and paste them all on the sidewalk in front of city hall in the shape of a one finger salute."

"Mom?" said Natalie. "Is there anything going on next weekend?"

"Hmm?"

"Have you made plans?"

"For next weekend?"

"You and dad could come out to the university and see what they've done to the bridge."

"Next weekend?"

"If you like."

"I… I don't know. I'd have to look at the calendar to be sure. I can never remember what we've promised to do."

"Will you let me know?"

"There!" said Mary, pointing over her father's shoulder at a rise in the road ahead. To one side was a small rocky outcrop, on top of which stood a row of sumac.

"You think?" said Carl.

"I think."

"All right," and he began to slow the car.

"And I know which painting."

"Hold on. Remember, we wait to see what the spot suggests."

At the top of the rise Carl pulled onto the shoulder and they all stepped out and looked around. Here was a good spot to spread out the picnic and Nola and Natalie got to work on this. Roberta stood by the car looking out over the fields below. Carl and Mary went a little ways up the outcrop and studied it a moment.

"What do you think?" asked Carl.

"I think what I thought before, if that's all right?"

"What? That I'm a fool?"

"No. That I know which painting goes here."

"Okay, kiddo. Go get it."

And off she went to the trunk of the car. When she came back to her father's side she held an abstract that looked something like a fish in blues and greens with a warm band approaching a yellowy-orange blended into its middle. There was something happy about it. Not joyous, but joyful. Kinetic, living.

She set it on the outcrop as high as she could reach. It listed to one side but they left it that way and stood back and puzzled over it for a while, admiring.

A couple of cars slowed as they went past in the road behind them, but although a couple of heads turned, neither car lingered.

"I like it," said Carl. "I think it's just right."

A little later, sitting at their lunch, they were fairly quiet for a spell, quiet for them, and when they were nearly done, just before beginning to clear away, Carl said, "You know, you're right. This Emmental really doesn't have much flavour." He looked at Nola. "I was thinking I was going to try it and then have some clever thing to say, like, 'Hey, it's not bland, it's subtle.' But you know, I think it's little better than eatable rubber," and he tossed the remaining bite across the road. He took a handful of grapes.

"Now these... These are good."

Just then another car approached. It slowed and came to stop. The window rolled down. A woman in sunglasses slid them down her nose and pointed to the painting on the outcrop.

"That for sale?" she said.

"Sorry," said Carl. "Just for looking at."

Nicco Pandolfi
STAYING PUT

From our toes, the taproots
we shot upon transplanting
anchor with a stranger

gravity, somehow stronger
than the sum of downward
Newtons, yet not enough

to hold us entirely. Still
our seeking tendrils wind
in ever wilder arcs,

though the object of their
grasping hovers just
beyond the frame.

All of which is to say
that this is simply not
our language, the tongues

of trunks and branches
tacit, withholding
old wisdom we

willfully abandoned
to build our world
of steel and glass.

Wish tilth wander
solar axon bloom?
you rightly ask,

as though I forgot
the question whose steady
echo in my ether

keeps me only ankle-deep
in honest loam. One day I
hope to wake and discover

a plant that can do the
talking for me, every
suburban defector's dream.

Mariya Deykute
ROOT

for Adina

she says Melbourne & means tree
tells me of houses like arrows stretched
to make room for the wind; all green
bottlebrush dripping scarlet
like a promise

she says the house was useless
but then I saw the tree & I wonder how
many trees have I loved & left
left so thoroughly I've forgotten
to miss them

she says and the ocean, of course
but all I want is to lean against bark
hear my grandmother's voice
really, all of my best friends
are trees

what do I root for, rootless, rooting
for my own self in this parade
of homes; stuck in the city
where the trees fail to grow
against the wind

against it, too, we stumble, up-
rooted; I want to tell her about the tree
I was given for my wedding, the umbrella
pine; how I wish we left it in the backyard
of our first house

instead of potting it & dragging it
& tending it clumsily; how we should have
remembered instead of trying to keep
how the wind whipped it dead
in the desert

we painted it white & set my veil about it
like a shroud; & it was a shroud year
we buried root after root after root
planting hardy, survivor trees
next to granite

but in Melbourne the tree still grows
even if it had been cut or rot got to it;
in her words it grows & she misses it
& there isn't anybody to tell her
if the tree isn't there

so if I write here: after they left a miracle
happened: the dead roots sprouted a sapling
one built for the desert & its terrible moods
who will care to tell me it isn't so, everyone
we knew has moved or died

allow me the secret life of roots
left; allow me my grandmother still
waving at me from the fourth's floor
I don't need to walk up, or see, just
promise me

Hayley Bowen
PORTIONS FOR FOXES

It is not in a vixen's nature
to abandon her young. Some ancient thing
decided long ago on her behalf
that she would be a mother.
But the instinct to survive is stronger.
So when the rancher's wife found the fox,
her back leg a tangle of blood and barbed wire,
she let it go. She knew there must be pups nearby.
But with a ruined leg,
all twisted muscle and rust,
a fox cannot hunt enough
to feed herself and her pups,
she cannot spy, belly low, on the hens in the yard—
if she stays here she will starve.
She retreats to the tall grass
that laces the edge of the woods, leaving
her den behind her. If she stays
they will all starve.

They will not learn to leap and dive
like land-borne salmon through waves
of ambering grain—a gold lake
in the September sun.
They will not learn to hunt, to creep
quietly in the blind spots of rabbits,
and they will starve to death—
withdrawals from their mother's milk—
before their brand-new eyes even have time
to open.
The den will cave in with the snow
and their bodies will unite with the roots
of the brambles that grow
overhead, marking the graves then
spreading so wild you'd never know
the flesh below that feeds them.

Catherine Con
TO THE FLOWERS

My mother—small and plump, the bang of her salt-and-pepper short bob draped over her long black and glinting eyes—woke me early on Thursday morning, about ten days after the announcement of the college entrance exam results. I was eighteen. She said she wanted to eat breakfast with me.

"What for?" I moaned in half-sleep, sulking. I wasn't ready to get up; I had just finished a detective novel and drifted into muted dreams three hours ago.

"What's she up to now? Didn't I just pass that darn exam?" I groaned as I got out of bed. I didn't know why she was making such a fuss over breakfast; we never ate breakfast together. Most of my time in the last four years was dedicated to study, more study, and more study, exercise, eating well for the one goal of passing the college entrance exam. Parties, outings, and vacations were put in the background. The exam took place during the summer after high school. The names of the students who succeeded were posted in the national newspaper; I was one of them. Like a balloon puffed up to the point of explosion which is suddenly deflated, I collapsed into a mostly nocturnal slump: sleeping past noon. When I was awake, I flipped wearily through the channels of the small black-and-white television in the corner of my room. Even though that indolent time felt like an eternity, it lasted only about a week.

"Well, get up, breakfast is getting cold," my mother said. It was the morning after three or four days of torrential rain. She had the windows open; the smell of wetness and the fragrance of tea floated in the air. We ate together, or rather, she ate, in silence, while I sipped tea.

"Oh, I signed you up for Japanese flower arrangement classes on Thursday nights. It's six-thirty to seven-thirty. Eat early tonight and shower so you can go join the class. You know, that flower shop two blocks from home on the corner." She tried to sound casual, but I could detect that slow, agitated tone in her voice. What the heck?

"Mom, when we bought flowers for your birthday, you complained how pricey it was and forbade us to do it again. Now you are signing me up for these expensive lessons, paying for the flowers and the instructions. Mom, you know only the wealthy ladies living in the twelfth-floor penthouses go to those fancy lessons." I put down my teacup and sighed. I didn't know what she was trying to do.

She turned to the maid. "Please make a soft egg, a little bit wet, with oyster mushroom for her." That was my favorite breakfast egg. The oyster mushroom consistency was like that of the cucumber flowers in the back garden of my childhood home. There, behind our old red brick house, the flowers of the vegetables and fruits blossomed in the warm rain. When there were too many blossoms, the maid cut the flowers and sautéed them. I especially loved the cucumber flowers stir-fried with eggs in the mornings; a baby cucumber in the sautéed egg gave an unexpectedly refreshing crunch. The nostalgic aroma of egg and mushroom; the quivering, shining yellow and white melded on a blue plate; a few sprinkles of black pepper—I gobbled up all the soft egg and mushroom in a few gulps. A quick smile flashed across my mother's stern face.

After breakfast, I noticed my mother didn't go to work as usual. She directed me to clean my room, change my sheets, and fold my clothes; showed me how to wipe down the dust on the closet, the study desk, and bookshelves; then had me take all the dirty laundry to the maid.

"You clean your dorm room like this," she said. After that, we went shopping for some clothes. When we stepped out of our apartment building, the bright mid-morning sun and the subtropical heat overwhelmed me. I felt faint; I hadn't been outdoors for months. I stood motionless, closed my eyes, and held my head with my hands for a moment to still myself. My mother looked severe and I wondered if I had done something wrong. At dinner, she put extra shrimp and broccoli in my bowl and watched me until every grain of rice was eaten. I tipped the bowl to show her an empty bowl. Those x-ray beams from my mother's eyes followed me to the bathroom. I could sense her gaze through the bathroom door while I showered, scrubbed behind my ears, and washed my hair.

"Want me to escort you to the flower shop?" she gently asked.

"No, I will go by myself."

That would have been very uncomfortable, to be dragged by my mother down the elevator and across the street, to be seen by those nosy neighbor ladies. I hurried, dried my hair, put on my shoes, and took the elevator down to the street. I walked in the balmy breeze of the summer evening to the flower shop, semi-dazed with a full stomach and the afterglow of a nice lukewarm shower.

It was indeed a fine, lovely shop, filled with gorgeous summer blooms; orange oleander, red hibiscus, and white gardenia zigzagged and overlapped around a small pond that I had never noticed. The old garden that was long frozen in my secret heart started to thaw. One tiny green shoot tentatively sprouted. I was that muddy kid sucking the azaleas' pistils. That sprawling old red brick house slumbered by rice paddy fields in the Taichung Basin on the island of Taiwan. Back of the house a large garden was enclosed by a low crumbling wall, which ran along the shallow river. Gold woodland foxglove, with its clumps of yellow bell-shaped blooms and opulent green leaves, clung to the mudbrick of the wall. Half of the lofty magnolia by the river struck by lightning had dried up; the living half vigorously yielded gorgeous white blossoms all year long. The blood-red azalea bushes under the magnolia were where I lingered. I scrambled over the mudbrick wall and collected the flowers into a large empty noodle bowl. When the bowl was filled with inflamed blossoms, I sat in the shade of the magnolia, and gently twisted and pulled the pistils out of the flowers to suck on them. They were sweet and moist, and quenched my thirst after long afternoons in the sun. I was a scrawny girl with short dark hair and large beady black eyes in my white shirt and blue jumper; my mother dressed me in blue and white for Mother Mary's protection. When I came in from outside, I'd have flower petals on my hair, and leaves, twigs, and mud on my tanned legs. My mother rinsed my arms and legs down with the well water she pumped into a dried gourd scoop. She called me a flower girl.

More than half of the flower-arranging class was over by the time I snapped out of my daydream, and the instructor had demonstrated a half-done arrangement. I tried to catch up with her, fumbling with the materials in front of me. When the class was over, the instructor came over to me and put all my materials, flowers, and leaves into a plastic bag.

"Is the first class difficult?" She smiled amiably. "Practice at home to catch up for next time, okay?"

"Okay," I said. The pink twilight filtered through the Japanese maple by my seat. I went home with the plastic bag hung from my shoulder. The walk home was short; I wanted a long and wide sidewalk where I could run and jump. Instead of taking the elevator, I capered up eight flights of stairs to get to our flat. My mother was pleased to see me panting and red.

"I couldn't catch up with the instructor," I said.

"It's okay, just the first class," my mother said, delighted. Her face now bore its usual calm and radiance. She pulled out all the materials from the plastic bag.

"Okay. There are always three main stems in an Ikebana arrangement, symbolizing heaven, human, and earth. Heaven is the longest, the main branch. The second branch is about three-quarters of the length of the main one and it symbolizes human. The third one is about half of the longest one and it is the Earth." My mother prattled on and on, animated. She was back to her normal self. The impression of my mother being once a young maiden arranging flowers was foreign to me. An enormous gush of affection for her surged up in me. I went up to her, towering over her, spotting the gray roots at the center of her crown. I swooped her pudgy waist into my arms, held up her hand in my palm and I twirled her, and I sang, and I giggled, and I heard the bird song, and I caught a whiff of the magnolia blooms, and she gave me a startled look of alarm and surveyed around our feet as we spun.

*

A sudden jerk of my heart, tears filled my eyes. I froze in front of Pablo Picasso's exhilarating painting "First Step" of a mother and child. We were at my daughter's university freshman orientation; together we toured the art gallery on her campus. In this painting, the anguished cubic face of the mother captures the essence of my mother's face that summer after my college entrance exam. And the child in the painting, in her bare feet, is eager to break free from her mother. Her beady black eyes, large with anxiety, look out to the world. Her body contorts with the strenuous exertion of using her legs for the first time; her face is a complicated mixture of tense anticipation and the delight of freedom; her upturned mouth suggests joy in her new independence. The mother, her supple round body in black dress and black shoes, gently props the child's hands in her hands, assists her in her tentative first step. Eyes downcast, her brows gathered, the mother is concerned, grave, in this vital moment of her child's life.

"Careful, put your left foot out, make sure it's a firm hold, and then your right foot," she says. She is letting her child go, helping her with her first step and then her second, and on from there. Would the world's excitement confuse the child on her path? When should she let go? Not now, not yet. And how much should she let go? Right now, maybe let go one hand, and then later the other hand. The mother's body is proportionally smaller in contrast to the child's in the painting; the mother withdraws to the background, yielding, letting the child evolve, move forward, take over the larger front part of the canvas. The child, in her blue and white sailor's suit, pushes her left hand off her mother's left palm, is ready to take off in her sailboat and claim the world.

In my blurred vision, I could see white magnolia and yellow foxglove scattered all around this flowerless painting.

Robin Gow
ROADSIDE AMERICA

Night falls on Roadside America every thirty minutes. Stars light up on the large room's ceiling and houses' windows glow yellow in the miniature village woven with toy train railways. As darkness descends on the room, we find each other; my brother Billy and I stand on either side of Uncle Rich. We don't say anything and around the room other families are doing the same—gazing out at the little town that could easily be their own.

I've always told people my Uncle Rich is my second dad. In Kutztown where I grew up the two are often confused with each other though I don't think they look alike. Dad has short blackish greying hair and Rich is bald with tufts of hair on either side. All Dad's dress shirts were given to him by Uncle Rich; Rich cares about looking nice. He cuts his own hair in a huge mirror on his side of our shared duplex.

I looked like my uncle and my dad even before hormones reshaped my body to resemble them more closely. It's something about the roundish shape of our faces and our dark blocky eyebrows. I wear patterned button-ups and earrings most days. I paint my nails deep blues and glittery blacks. I cut my own hair over the bathroom sink in my New York City apartment.

Growing up, summers belonged to us: Billy, Uncle Rich, and me. We went to zoos, amusement parks, and museums, but I remember Roadside America in the most detail. It was really just a stop on the way to Cabela's. The whole display couldn't have been much larger than my apartment but it felt like we stayed there for hours. Maybe we did. That was back when Billy was really into trains. I was more concerned with the miniatures.

Once, I leaned over and told Rich, "Someday I want to live somewhere that looks just like that." It's funny because I now live in the complete opposite of that town—New York City, where night never falls gentle or patiently—where a train calls on through till morning. The sun is tired here. There are no yellow windows.

He said something like "It reminds me of where I grew up" or "Isn't it nice?" Maybe we had this conversation more than once. Maybe we had it each time we visited Roadside America. We'd take turns pointing out different parts we noticed. Billy called us over to observe the blooms of steam coming from the engines and the gold trim around their wheels. I showed them a little girl no bigger than my thumbnail—her blonde pigtails perfectly symmetrical. Rich wondered aloud how long it must have taken to construct a world like this. He gestured to the painted mountains and the swathe of green trees. I imagined the town as perpetually mid-July: the depths of summer where the days leaked into each other and the sun rose and set in what felt like thirty minutes. We could live there between humid days and cool encircling nights. We could walk into the intricately decorated corner store and buy candies from clear glass jars. We could watch as the trains wove themselves across our gravel roads and then back up into the mountains.

I used to think of Uncle Rich as a kind of savior. I don't feel like this now, but when Dad was cruel or angry, I would imagine a world where Uncle Rich was my dad. I remember once Mom brought up that one day Rich might have "his own family." I told her I wouldn't like that. I didn't want to share Rich. Sometimes I wonder if he wishes he had his own kids. Were we enough?

I'm not sure when Rich started watching Fox News. Maybe he always had and it was something I didn't pick up on until I'd moved away from home. I started to notice the talking points floating into everyday conversations when I'd visit. He'd say things like, "people should come here legally," or, more towards my direction "no one respects the institution of marriage anymore." When he said these things, his tone would change—sharp and angry in a way I'd never associated with him. The first time I came home wearing a chest binder, I heard him say "sex is a biological fact." The grey binder crushed my body tight underneath a green V-neck. I looked at myself in the bathroom mirror and heard Uncle Rich and my father's voices warped in the living room. How had I not noticed this? I thought to myself, somehow feeling like it was my fault, because I left.

When I visit, I often sit at the kitchen counter and the family moves around me like a projection. Sometimes I only feel real inside myself as their chorus of "she, her, hers" buzzes around me. But I have learned I can re-enter the family in small ways. Sometimes I make Uncle Rich coffee. He smiles and thanks me before going to sit on the warped polka-dot sofa. I offer to drive him to work up the street. I tell him about scary movie I've seen recently. Really though, these feel like distractions, like I'm trying to find something for us to say to each other that will gloss over the fact that my body is different and I don't look like the bright freckle-faced girl he took on day trips in the summer.

Roadside America's website states the display hasn't been altered since its completion in 1963 when its creator, a Mr. Laurence Gieringer, passed away. The structure began in his home but soon became too large for the place to hold it.

Is a life the story of outgrowing more and more spaces? No, maybe "outgrowing" isn't the right word. For so long I thought I outgrew my childhood home as I sat in my bedroom writing stories and poems that whirled away from reality. I thought I outgrew whatever connection I had with my uncle. I thought I had moved on and learned to recognize the kinds of prejudice and hatred he had inside him. I told myself I wasn't like him. I wasn't like them. I was a queer trans person whether or not he used my name or believed. What is a truer way to describe this? Maybe I fractured a miniature image he had of me—a woman with a long flowing dress and the pixie haircut I had in high school, standing in a quiet street in a diorama town.

Roadside America's display itself has ten thousand handmade trees and six hundred lightbulbs. So much detail. So much care. A man's movements grew and live still. Night falls. The sun rises. The people never age. The store never runs out of candy. The trains take the same paths each day. I wonder what it takes to clean and keep Roadside America running. What do the people who work there think of it? Do they cherish the small town like we did? There must be constant maintenance to keep the town alive. Wires to be checked. Switches to fix. Train wheels to grease.

I tell myself Uncle Rich has to know who I am despite it all—that he loves me. He knows what it was like to crouch down and peer into tiny miniature homes—to dream ourselves into a brilliant fantastical unchanging town. I press my face to the glass around the display. I point to a painted herd of cattle. I tell him they look like the ones that roam behind our house. He tells me that could be our house—that it almost looks like our home.

Randall R. Freisinger

THAT WHICH HE MIGHT HAVE DONE HE DID NOT DO

—after a painting by Ivan Albright

Beyond the sleepless thrum of Vegas a man
parks near a narrow bridge and gazes down
into a steep chasm, its river's black slither
barely visible far below. This bridge
one of the places to which he's returned. Places
where once he'd peeled away this or that
layer of self in a determined search for bedrock.
His plan of late had been to make amends
with each of those selves he long ago abandoned,
but most by now had vanished, or refused
to take him back, his drinking self the sole
exception, the only one willing to admit
he'd been missed and willing to reconcile.
To be sober or not—what had it really mattered?
There's nothing good or bad but drinking
makes it so, he thinks, staring down, trying
to imagine how such a gash had been created,
the magnitude of wind's persistence, water's
unhurried work. The gorge this morning still
hides in shadow. As he continues to stare,
heat building around him like a potter's kiln,
he thinks about depth and angles, the interval
of sunlight that visits the abyss only briefly
each day, much as in his own managed waste
of a life—that time between last drink and first,
those few quiet moments before his mind
remembers it has forgotten to think.
He tips a small flask to his lips, toasts
the trickle of river below, then the breadth
of desert stretching vast and cracked
all around him, flat, relentlessly exposed.
Isn't topography itself, he wonders,
a form of dream, full of meanings, manifest

and latent? Which better: a life running
in the open or one fetal, tucked in perpetual dusk?
A false choice, he knows, but, most of his life
drawn to false choices, he's come to believe
they expose, in their very falsity, a smatter of truth:
the horned dilemma of life itself. A good place
to stop, he decides, so he bookmarks it
with another drink, elevating his flask
of cheap vodka, gifting the gods above,
absolving the deepening darkness below.

—For My Brother, 1937-1977

Paul Luikart

GOON

Back in Thunder Bay where I grew up, a place where every kid on the block including me was crazed with pro-hockey dreams, we played pond hockey. Every afternoon after school, every winter. Once, in a game in fifth grade, I went hard after the puck with one of my little buddies hot on my tail. I slid to a stop and just as I corralled the puck, the ice cracked, and I splashed through. It took me a second to realize I was standing up to my waist in frigid water. My buddies laughed while I struggled out and when the tears bloomed in my eyes, they went crazy. I hobbled home, fast as I could, still in my skates. My pop said, "Hockey pros don't cry. Besides, think about it this way: You fall through lake ice, you'd be dead in five minutes. So, be glad."

If you're a hockey fan, here's something you know: Wayne Gretzky scored 894 goals in his career, the most ever. Plus, he had the most assists: 1,963. Plus, pages and pages of other high marks, nearly all of which are also in the "most ever" or "best ever" categories. And that's not to mention his four Stanley Cups.

But, here's something you didn't know: I've got Gretzky beat in a few categories. Most noses broken? That's me. Three million. The lumps on my knuckles prove it. Busted jaws: Two million. One million upper cuts, and the other million on hooks to the jawbone. The docs use tweezers to pick bone shards out of the other guy's sinus cavity. And then, all hail the Concussion King. I dished out a few hundred thousand. Remember my second stint with the Leafs, the game where I clobbered Pierre Patterson and they hauled him off the ice on a gurney? Last I heard, his wife has to wear a name tag because of how often he forgets who she is.

It's not like I haven't taken my licks too. How many times has my nose gotten busted? Don't know anymore. How many times have I been handed a broken jaw? Lost count. How many concussions have I gotten? Numbers don't go that high. When Alexi Kuznetsov played for the Blues, he got a good one in on me with his stick. Right in the back of the neck, just below my helmet. Whack! They said my head hit the ice like a medicine ball and I almost went through the boards. I missed the rest of the season because of that motherfucker.

Like me, Kuznetzov retired a year back. Soon after, he found Jesus. Imagine that. Guys get into a lot of different things when they step off the ice forever. Hunting trips, business start-ups, a few run for office, more than a few have managed used car lots. But religion is, let's say, unusual. Funny thing though, last week he called me up. Since I retired from the Blackhawks and I liked Chicago, I stayed in the city. Kuznetzov had moved to Tampa Bay, he told me, gotten married, had a kid on the way, and joined a church. Not one of those fancy ones with golden spires like they have all over Moscow—where he's from—but one that meets in a building that used to be a grocery store.

"Look," he said, in that thick Russian accent, "I call you for serious reason. I call to say I am sorry. For slashing you in back of the head."

I pretended I had to remember what he was talking about, even though, a couple nights ago, that hit broke into my dreams again and I woke up drenched and gasping.

Finally, I said, "Well, don't think twice about it. It's hockey. Shit happens."

"I could have hurt you very badly."

"But you didn't, and it's—"

"I'm asking for you to forgive me."

"Forgive you? For the whack?" The words leapt out in a high-pitched scoff before my brain could filter them. I worry that I'm getting slower, mentally. That the gaps between my brain cells are getting wider and that, eventually, those gaps—that mental nothingness—will corrode my whole brain. I'll become a babbling shithead who can't take a piss without a crew of nurses to help him find his pecker.

"I mean, that's not a problem. Sure I do." There was a long pause. Or maybe it just felt like a long pause. I blurted, "Did I ever do anything to fuck you up?"

"No, no."

"If I did, you know, the same goes for me."

We chatted a few more minutes and I even said congratulations on everything. The wife, the kid, the new-found religion. Then we said goodbye and I wondered if I'd ever see him again in my life. 'Sorry' has always had a bitter taste to me. I'm not opposed to taking responsibility for one's own shit, mind you. I was glad for his call. But, "I'm sorry," makes me shiver.

I've never wanted to be "born again." Since I retired, I realized one life is enough. More than enough. I plied my trade on the ice as a goon. I wasn't hired to score goals or rack up points. I wasn't even hired to win Stanley Cups. I was hired to break faces and spill blood. I signed the very first contract they offered me without negotiating for an extra dime. Which probably says something about the value of the soul I piloted around the NHL for ten seasons. For every nose I smashed, I bet God or the universe or whatever peeled a day off the end of my life and chucked it onto the eternal shit pile. Like justice or karma.

And after I retired, for awhile, I figured, 'What's the point in waiting around?' My purpose, such as it was, had been fulfilled. Two months after my last game, I even wrote up a little note: "I had a nice life, but it's over now. I'm sorry to everybody I ever hurt." The plan was to chug Jim Beam and Tylenol until the reaper showed up. I downed plenty of whiskey, but I couldn't bring myself to throw back the pills. I woke up in my Lay-Z-Boy and barfed on the rug. What would Brother Kuznetsov say?

This winter is the first I haven't played hockey since I was two years old. My bedroom window looks out over Lake Michigan. I've taken to strolling along the frozen beach, gliding over the wide, ice-filled furrows of sand, and letting my mind wander. I'll walk out on the jetty where the freezing wind nearly picks me up and drops me onto the huge jags of ice piled up against the concrete. A smack, and a crack, and a broken back. They'd find me in the springtime, washed up on the sand, with the gulls and crows pecking out my eyeballs.

I think I'm visiting Lake Michigan—a veritable no-man's land in winter—because I'm waiting for something to happen. I think about lacing on my skates and zipping across the lake as far as I can until either I fall through and disappear forever or wind up washed up on the Michigan sand dunes. But something funny happens when you stand at the end of a jetty, staring out at a huge, frozen lake. Sure, it's ice, frozen and solid. Two feet thick in some places, especially near the beach where it's shallow. But if you watch closely, you can see the ice rise and fall in slow, wide swells. The lake is breathing. Massive and silent, it's alive. Regardless of any ideas I might have about what is happening or what could or should happen in my life—such as it is, an-ex goon, cap in hand—something is definitely happening. Or, rather, something is happening again that has always happened and will keep on happening forever.

Carrie George
LEFTOVERS

My bones: salted and iridescent
on the Atlantic's tongue, hollow
like a ripe watermelon
or a cage. My skin,
inside-out, cherry jelly—
lumpy but sweet, red.
My lungs crumble
like coral in black oil.
My lips severed from my face
like a cliff's edge—nothing
to say now.
I ask to be cut
in pieces. My femur left
as driftwood in the waves.
Each thumb wrenched whole
to be dinner for the whales.
Let the length of my hair bake
like sand, my nails sliced
thin as mica tumbling
in the river current.
Grow me small in
my second life,
no bigger than
an egg of a cardinal fish
waiting in the sea grass
for time to hatch and kiss
the feet of plastic carcasses
floating brave as life
in the shrinking shores.
Give me back
to the cracked floor,
a front-row seat as the mouth
of the world lifts
and shows our sorry bodies
what its teeth were made
to endure.

Chris Ketchum

SELF-PORTRAIT AS PANTRY

A yam sprouts Hydra heads,
purple ruffles garnishing opal necks.
Shed gowns of garlic shift
in the overhead fan's tiny wind.
Assorted, dusty cans clutter
the shelf with its red-checkered lining:
A greased tin of pinto beans;
coconut milk, lite, with a blue wrap
stacked on the stewed tomatoes
for which I've no use, no recipe, no plan
and never have.

Maybe she left them behind
when she left, steered her bullet
-colored Ford over Canada's northern plains.
She called today,
two weeks after I chased her to Anchorage
with a mind in parted states,
and when I said, *It's okay,* she said,
But it's not, and I thought
we'd loved ourselves into sickness.
After each *Goodbye, No-Need-*
to-Call, the morning's inevitable collapse
of will flared red and green—end
or accept—like a newly begotten infection.

I google uses for stewed tomatoes
and *foodnetwork* says, *Stew*. I shave my face
until, again, it's blank. I help myself
to myself three times before breakfast.
When hunger returns me
to the cabinet, I set aside the lentil jars
and reach for the furthest crevice:
a yellow diadem on fluted glass,
its label reading

DYNASTY
PURE SESAME OIL
FOR ORIENTAL SEASONING

and remember the fat, heirloom wedges
        she cut this summer, dressed
in a smoky garment of soy and oil,
        and arranged on a plate like a bruise
in capricious stages: crimson, scarlet, vermillion
        rouging the dish with juice—

She'd never buy tomatoes brined
        in their own fluid.
She'd never lock a thing in the cell of itself.
        What would be the use?

Jeremy Gregersen

SISTINE NOTEBOOKS: JOEL

American Natural History Museum, NYC

> *"That which the palmerworm hath left hath the locust eaten;*
> *and that which the locust hath left hath the cankerworm eaten;*
> *and that which the cankerworm hath left hath the caterpillar eaten..."*
> *--JOEL 1:4*

Everything here angles to eschatology.
The dusty armaments of a hundred thousand things
that found their many ends some season centuries ago,
fossils hermetically held under glass by glints

of bent wire. Jack lets go my hand, leaving the "boring
bones" behind, and runs to the stairs following signs
to the dinosaurs he's sure we've come to see.
I catch up to him and scan over his shoulder

a plaque, an etched timeline of Jurassic beasts,
and follow his finger to the black silhouette
of a man crammed in the corner for scale.
"Everything here is dead but him,"

Jack says and looks up at the bones of an allosaur
posed as poised to eat the boy—though, I suppose,
no skeleton's ever benign.
We move on to the third floor's dioramas

and find a zebra, shot and gutted
a generation back and posed to die
forever, its curling lip somehow glistening yet,
somehow its tufts of mane remain erect, somehow

stuffed and ever bleeding wet into the claws
and maw of a lion killed and stuffed
to kill forever, its amber eyes focused
not on the kill but on some middle distance,

maybe to mark the approach of some greater threat.
I look over my shoulder to check that we're safe
for a time. Tired, we leave the museum
and its dangers behind. Descending the steps

toward the Park we're met by some wild Joel
making his way up 77th from the Broadway side,
all eyes, balding and beardless, ragged pea coat
predicting doom and judgment, the smoking crater

from which none will rise. Jack takes my hand again
as if to comfort me, to say that there's nothing
novel in the noise of things prophesied,
that we should pay no mind,

for while not all signs are the damp and ragged
cardboard kind, we should know by now
that the end of something or everything
is, as ever, nigh.

Todd Heldt
BACKFLOW

--the phenomenon in which the probability flows
in the opposite direction to the momentum

The quantum particles of the rat
cleave and fall into new disorder
and trip down the sidewalk and into
the café he'd just left, climb on
the barstool and say to his ex-,
a noted scientist, I'm not done
with my drink yet. Please wait.
And then the conversation continues
backwards from there: Go. Don't.
You love I? And the words before
that would stumble--something
about what they had meant
to one another but how once uncaged
love can't be locked up again.
Before that were more words
about things that had happened
in the lab or what they'd been up to
pacing their separate hallways,
she a successful biologist,
and he a lab rat on which
she had once performed
experiments, but also
with whom she had fallen in love,
and their awkward but mutually
gratifying courtship. For a while.
Of course, it all happens in reverse
this time and would be hard to understand
if you were seeing it, which of course
you wouldn't be because it occurs
at the subatomic level.
Isn't love weird? Always falling
on the faces of the unexpecting

and the incompatible, out of the sky
and then bouncing out of reach,
like a balloon scoffing at the laws
of thermodynamics, refusing
to do what you think it ought,
or like conversations that come up
again and again, and are both
past and present. Nothing new
to add to this, whatever it was
we disagreed about, just seeing
if this is still who we are, and
wondering if we will ever go back
to the place when we were.
Eventually against the reason
of distance and days we are in
her apartment kissing
for the first time, dreaming of what
we could become, and even then
the death of us is seeping
into our skin. How small we are
that probability and momentum are love
now and then.
We are written and erased
by people we are not. Don't laugh.
It's all we get, and I am he, and
you are I, a rat in search of a reason,
a science to which you can donate
your body that loves and dies.

Chris Ketchum
MIRAGE

On the beach, Jon says he's met a lover,
icing his feet in the tide. Water lunges
toward a sandy buttress, breaks white
and lolls back into itself, his dark hair
a spur wet-sketched along his metatarsal.

If things work out with Emily, then—
Sometimes he finishes that sentence.
Other times he stops to watch the wind
tumble hues of molten light together
on Lake Michigan's blue-halogen top—

It's the blue of Capital Market's *Open*
sign where I used to buy him beer
for the bets I was always losing:
A twenty-two of Dead Guy Ale because
I said I'd shave my head, then wouldn't.

Got drunk and tried to box him once, but
he quit before I blacked out. Told Laura
that I'd make a life with her. I couldn't.
I always planned the end before it started.
Walking the tide-shoved bank beside him,

I say I'm happy he's found someone. I want
for Jon a kind of love I'm not sure I believe in:
Lifetime-guarantee love. Down-payment
-free love. This-coupon-never-expires love.
Love backed by the FDIC. I tell Jon

how I've met a lover, too, and, for once,
I'm trying not to meet another one.
He stares down the shoreline at an island
rippling in distorted light effused
by the cobalt surface—the way heat

simmers on a car's hood, warping air. I bet
the island's a mirage, like how the mirrored
lake reshapes a far-off dune to an hourglass.
He bets that it's not—thinks we can make
the peninsula before sundown, where land

falls away into the lake. *You'll always find*
an end if you're looking for one. I ask him
how he could be so sure. He says, *I'm not,*
then nods along the lakerim where the beach
curves out of sight—which means we'll walk,

god knows how far, until we're out of shore.
Tell her, these are the ways I'm broken,
he says. I say, *What are.* Facing the point,
he almost smiles, sand graying in the light
like ash, slipping invisibly down to the water.

Phillip Sterling
EDAPHIC

Imagine you're on the far shore of a Great Lake
where the woods are demented by unfamiliar soil

—as if you were impoverished, far from home,
and upon waking found yourself on the wrong side

of a low-budget mattress, transient and confused,
unsure as to which direction the sun will appear,

if it appears at all, or whether the dream you just
woke from, a dream of prairie and wild ponies,

of endless, star-striven sky, were a dream at all
—and morning a strange, whiny dog beside the bed

(a fussy, probing hound that wants something,
obviously, though you're not sure what, as

it's not your dog, whose needs are more easily
read: *Yap*, to be let out; *Yip*, to get up on the bed).

Or—and isn't this more likely?—that the dream
from which you're about to rise may not be

dream at all, but a language you have yet to learn.
Listen carefully. The lake will acknowledge you,

or it won't. It will speak or remain mute.
It cares nothing for your idleness and confusion,

your sunless slump. Your lingering in bed a bit
longer, on the edge of a dream, one way or another,

will convey neither good nor harm with regards to
the astonishment of water before you, the great

puddle that was here in the darkness when you
arrived and which, it being April and resurrection

certain (if somewhat demented), will translate as
shore or *horse* long after the woods return to dirt.

Sydney Bollinger
SHORELINE

We sipped coffee, taking in the sound of the morning's high tide lapping against the sand. He would meet me out here, eyes set on the horizon, waiting for the sun to make its humble ascent into the sky. Our old wicker chairs were our comfort of choice, despite being sticky with saltwater residue. Even in the summer heat, steam rose out of his mug and joined with the water hanging around us. My father and I relished these moments of morning serenity as we waited for the sun to join us overhead, as we waited to see the water turn its blue-gray hue.

He died ten years ago. Now, I spend my mornings on the deck alone.

With my coffee, I sit in his chair and cherish the sunrise because I know this is my last. Leaning forward, I reach my fingers out and touch the water. My ocean draws closer to me each day, and I wish I could greet her with joy and gratitude. Instead, I set my mug down and bow my head to God, clasping my hands together despite the humidity, the mugginess, the want to accept my fate and let her take me when the tide recedes. I want her to swallow me up and let me become part of the new natural order I helped create.

"Can I bring my things with me? Can I hire a mover?" I had asked when the men first came to my home. The pair of them sat across from me in my living room, wearing neon vests, holding a tablet.

"You won't have the space, ma'am," the blonde one said. My grip on the arm of my chair tightened, leading to white knuckles, an increased pulse, tension in my jaw.

"It'll only be a studio while we try to figure out what to do with y'all," the other one said, looking at his hands in his lap. When they first visited me, they had told me how I would only be able to bring a suitcase, that furniture would be provided, that I wouldn't have much time because the sea level is rising so rapidly, that this is a mandatory evacuation, but wait, don't call it that, it's not an evacuation, not really, it's a relocation, and the refugee camps, wait, wrong word, relocation center, I think, and ma'am, well, we need to take you to Kansas and we need to take you to Kansas within the week.

Standing up, my eyes never leave the ocean and I wish I could stay here until the tide never recedes back to the ocean, when my house becomes an island, the roof a refuge for birds, for shipwrecked travelers, for those who were not forcibly removed from their homes.

"Ma'am? It's time to go," the man shouts. I want to tell him "thank you" for allowing me to have one last morning coffee on my deck overlooking the ocean.

I grab hold to the suitcase handle and take a deep breath. "Goodbye," I whisper. "I'll see you again when you catch up to me."

Patricia Clark
EXAMPLES OF UNEASINESS

1. I struggled to unlock the door, arms loaded with what I carry with me each morning—canvas bag with a notebook, some paint brushes, a Bonnard art book, thermos, coffee mug—and something dark fell down as I opened the door. What was it? Wing of a bird, a bat? Did I even see it? I doubted myself. And then it was gone. Then, later, on my work table, a large dark brown spider appeared, at least three inches across. I saw it hop and that nearly undid me. I didn't think I could work with it there on the loose. I picked up a ceramic vase and trapped the spider underneath.

2. I had floaters in my left eye. It was distracting. Sometimes just a pinprick of black like a speck floating. Other times a string, a thread, a thin strand. I reached up to brush it away. It happened while I was driving.

3. I greeted a woman at an event. And then remembered, in an instant, that her husband had died recently. Spontaneously, then, "I'm so sorry about your husband. You must miss him." She's quite small and this night, smiling. I touched her shoulder. Later I remembered the story a friend told me, that this very woman had referred to a fellow traveler using the N word. Why did I forget that and remember about her husband? They were known to be quite wealthy. Her husband had invented a medical device that made him a fortune.

4. She called two times, no message. Then I called her and got stuck talking to her husband, someone I never liked. He wanted to put bars on their windows. He locked the doors at night from the inside with a key. She called me again but I was out. Missed connections. Her voice trembled with the message she left. I didn't know how to get through. She was my sister.

5. Doubts that I've been fair. Something I said to someone mentioning the famous man. Was he a monument, or a sex offender? Can a person be both? I don't know the whole picture. Do we ever?

6. I cling to a routine like a lifeline—a poached egg, an English muffin. A clementine a day. The same route driven to work. And still, a growing sense of dislocation.

7. Half of an oyster shell, like a chaise lounge, really. I can see a designer drawing a shape for later production. The fabric in an off-white silk. How the oyster would relax, lean back, all undressed. But could it be comfortably seduced there?

8. I hear news (at different times) that two men I loved have died. Though we hadn't communicated in years, they were in my mind at times as people are—and one, who I'd lived with in college, had written to me a few years ago, sending me a book I'd owned by Edmund Wilson, a few photographs (one of me smoking), and a photograph I'd taken of a bridge in a driving rain. Then I'd made a painting. It kindled nothing between us. I didn't write back.

9. Wine with dinner—trout and pinot noir. Then the after-meal when I read, often, or watch a news show. And then it's 11 p.m., the bloated feeling of waste, the wasted feeling of nothing accomplished or learned or discovered.

10. Driving home through downtown, and a sudden downdraft of dark birds, a huge flock of them under the freeway bridge. Where they roost, a beautiful surge down, a wave, and I almost flinch thinking the car will hit them, but no—they wing back up, all in a group, what is called a murmuration. And before I have passed them, they tilt, turn together, one way, then another, only a few inches between each of them, looking like a shape of a thrown cloak, or a cylinder in air, and then gone.

11. I live upstairs in an old neighborhood, rent a flat in a tall house. The stairs are steep. As my friends age, various ones can no longer visit me because of the stairs, their knees or hips. Two friends still come. What of the day I can no longer climb them? Or my friends no longer come?

12. I work and I read. I walk and I cook dinner. My appetite is not large and I pride myself in not gaining a pound. At a restaurant I watch a woman with red hair putting bread in her mouth, chewing it, reaching for more. It seems she cannot stop. When olive oil runs out, she asks for butter. I cannot stop watching her. Her jaws grind and grind.

13. I had a friend who would bring a stack of fragrant wood smelling of apples for my fireplace. One of his trees would fall and he'd cut lengths for me that fit in my small fireplace. He died in his sleep. I was the one who found him—half undressed, on his bed. Some music playing loud, I think it was Bruce Springsteen.

14. Sometimes I paint with music on or sometimes I choose silence. Applying the color after I've mixed paint, making a mark—it's my vision. I stand back from the canvas later and think "Where was I, in my mind?" Sometimes the answer is here, sometimes France. What I see is Provence, the golden fields of rapeseed, and then wisteria climbing on pergolas in the small villages, and then plane trees, pruned and shapely. Then stone of a Roman viaduct, dust, an olive tree someone says is 3,000 years old. People take selfies with it.

15. I've come to dislike autumn. I don't need reminders. It's terrible to lose the colors, verdant green especially, and have them replaced by dun, gray, black. A grisaille landscape. And it could end with this. I carried the spider outside and tipped over the ceramic vase. I turned my back on it.

Tim Hawkins
BORDER CROSSING

One morning far from home, twelve months on the road, sick and drinking
tea from a dirty cup and blowing on my hands to keep them warm,
young and romantic and feeling sorry for myself in Guangxi Autonomous
Region, where I'd crossed the border on foot from Lang Son, Vietnam.

Feeling full of myself, full of petty, intractable officials, full of freezing rain,
full of unsmiling border guards, full of bicycles laden with goods, full of *bai fan*
and small warm glasses of beer, full of the misery of being,
full of crowds at the station, the hostile PLA, and being stuck in Nanning,
two days before Christmas, 1991.

Full of hot pot with goose and ginger to numb my infected throat,
full of snake blood and seahorse rum, full of waiting and tedious cares,
full of bureaucrats and queues to outmaneuver and overcome
full of recently-legitimized capitalist merchants touting their wares,
and sleeping in a workers' dormitory to save a few *yuan*.

***

That morning I'm startled from my thoughts by a speaker truck blaring
and throngs of people hurrying to the square.
Three men dressed alike in blue and hatless in the cold,
their hands bound tightly behind their backs,
are bundled out of the truck to face the gathering crowd.

An official mans the bullhorn while two armed soldiers stand guard;
the harangue and collective response resound in *Bai hua,*
the local dialect, which I cannot understand. However, I'm told
the three are thieves, who will be driven up into the surrounding hills;
Their families will be billed for the bullets that end their lives.

Two gray-haired old ones slouch with eyes cast down,
perhaps calling up visions of lives nearly spent,
but the third is just a boy, who stands tall
and faces the chanting throng with a faraway look in his eyes
while the wind blows through him and keeps him from falling.

He sees what he sees; one bearded foreigner stands out in the crowd.
He fixes on that face as if it could somehow change the world,
as if it could change anything at all. However, there are no heroics,
no last minute reprieves. After the expiation of collective guilt,
the men are loaded in the truck and driven into the hills to their fate.

❊❊❊

Later that morning, still stuck in Nanning, still sick and drinking
tea from a dirty cup and blowing on my hands to keep them warm,
young and grateful to be alive in Guangxi Autonomous Region,
where I'd safely crossed the border on foot from Lang Son, Vietnam.

Feeling emptied of myself, emptied of self-pity and needless cares,
there is a oneness I feel with these multitudes of people,
a music to their chattering *Bai hua,* and a freshness in the air.
Even the ubiquitous short-haired Asian dogs are handsome
and the soldiers seem so young and far from home.

Abigail Goodheart
ELEGY FOR GEM CITY ROLLER DERBY PLAYER NO. 281

Driving through Ohio, sun setting, all the land backlit,

the little waves of cornfields grow mysterious

rolling hills reminding me of sea monsters:

I get seasick when landlocked.

This is what Einstein said space was like: waves,

stars among them, some collapse on themselves,

have you seen pictures of Dayton in the fifties?

Feeding and feeding on the space around it.

The first road off the highway is all strip mall, strip mall,

strip club, copper-stripped, boarded up.

In the roller rink, the bathroom is bubblegum pink, the other,
electric space blue. The rink has a mural of the solar system,
the whole thing glitters in the dark, skaters revolve on an axis,
evolve from a high school couple and their third wheeling friend
to a couple with a toddler on those skates that fit over his shoes.
Everyone is a little unwanted at the roller rink—

she spent a lot of time here; we have all spent a lot of time here.

Renee Agatep
OHIO

She belongs to her mother and the state of Ohio
I wish she belonged to me.
-- Damian Jurado, "Ohio"

That's no kind of romance,
Billy. See,
they tell me I'm
from Ohio. I
don't belong to any
mother there, no one looks out
slapping metal screen doors for my arrival and
when I leave, there's no barn dance, no
adorned tractors, only
my mother's ghost
stepping on rusted nails in Habitat
parking lots, dancing in truck stop strip clubs
and disappearing into the dust of gravel,
no Humanity at all.
Dentists' sons laugh in the
smell of manure, and jump ropes are made
nooses for the poorest
vermin on the stony-side playgrounds,
reserved for cold,
hazy, muddy,
memories.

That's no reason to get misty,
Billy. See,
I don't belong
to Ohio or
anyone else, and the winds
don't change – those
crumbled black fields

spinning in concentric squares, plowed
year after year by those same families
will always spiral down
into the dark
heart of it all.

Lizzy Drew

EARTH IN TWO DIMENSIONS

This earth is red-stained. For water, a week in any direction,
the air superheated and burrowing into my flared nostrils, my
cracking mouth. We see birds dead in heaps outside our house.
I move through their stiff bodies, use the rigor mortis bloat
as a grounding point; when my mother cooks them, we have
to scrape the dirt out of their feathers and their eyes. The dirt
seeps through the unfillable holes in the walls, and brings with it
disease. The house a mile down the road is a permanent influenza
recovery room. Our neighbors unboarded their window one
night and now the little one is coughing up pink pulp. I pretend
there's nothing scratching at my throat when I think of thirst. The
alternative is heaving, hunched over, cradling my folded body.
The whole of the crust is loose and fighting. My mother warned
me against greed and held her back to the wind. My mother
walked into a red-teethed wave and swallowed. On this earth, all
the cloth we have is for praying.

Michael Mark
THE CURL

My mother bends so close, her breaths
warm my tiny grandmother's cold cheeks,
whispers, *Hold still, mom,*

slips her fingers through the rings
of the cherished sewing scissors, pulls
the inch-wide wisp straight.

Here's where my mother stops her confession
of when my grandmother died, how before
she called anyone, her father, a doctor,

cried one tear, she took a curl.
She says she's saving it for me, and warns
I should not look for it yet.

When I find it she will be gone.
My mother returns to her mother,
to a small room twenty years away.

Will I keep it? Cupped in my palm,
will I breathe in the ancient powder
and broth? Will I fit my fingers

through the round eyes of those scissors,
ask my mother to be still?

Stuart James Forrest
AIN'T THAT THE WAY?

When good things happen,
I reach for the phone to call my mother.
When bad things happen,
I reach for the phone to call my mother.

She is gone.

Still, I reach out,
beyond me, this time, this world,
to that place, any place,
where she listens to me still.
Still listening, like a woman,
combing her child's hair,
humming to the radio,
on Sunday,
before we go to church.

Tristan Rivers

MIDNIGHT DOKUSAN AT NORTH GRAY DUNES

Mother's steps, uneven
one heavy, one light
room breathing
cottage lungs
Woodsmoke faint upon
hanging hickory

Freshwater moon
waves loud
in mind
Coals burn deep
in night sand
with
no one
to keep
watch

Ellen Stone

WINTER HAWK

When the broad-winged hawk
screeches her raspy cry
above fallow corn,
she sees everything
clearly spread below –
our trudging footprints
down the snowy slope,
loose sod beneath our weight,
iced prints of bobcat or fox
ahead. Her underbelly,
glints pearl, even in this
grey boil of cloud.

What moment
takes us sky-ward?
This wind-drift glider,
oak leaf aeronaut
lifts in her glossy
talons, holds
in this kettle of sky –
the chosen, elemental.
So contained, we two
stepping gingerly
across a crust of earth,
afraid to soar.

Nancy Squires
COMMUTER

If only if only I could sleep right now stay
here all morning no going no coming for what I am about to do
let me be truly grateful

the dark's the dark no matter how you slice it these lanes
we tumble down headlong headlit what's that about anyway
anyway any way you look at it

it's cold. Last night's dreams dying away still linger
I was trying to explain the sadness
of not only death but of waste and the awful

within us, slow surge of orchestra the soprano's crystal notes
brought me to tears no streetlights out here

my consciousness a screen now playing wind tree shadow
early morning darkness two eyes glowing from the pavement
the deer lying in the road

the deer lying in the road.

Betsy Johnson
HOW TO BE ALONE AND BE WELL

stones
should
stay
Outside

same
with
Roars

you
don't
want
This?

walk
the
Ditch

step
over
the
Dead

possum

Kevin Casey
ROCK PILE

The cinder block toed into the soil
behind the garden shed,
its two great eyes having watched
days beyond count come and go,

had been left forgotten for so long
among the rounded granite skulls
and sable books of shale
that it came to believe

it was also a stone, and shared
in their same self-assurance
that comes from idling beyond all use
in the shade of a hawthorn tree.

Maggie Walcott
I CARRY

You lean across the table to explain
with small hands, fine boned instruments of illumination
that you spent one interminably hot summer learning
a trowel's sharp lines and the pleasing sound metal makes
when scraping mortar across brick

how you spent the next seven summers learning
that tool belts are the portable version of a car's back seat
after a week-long vacation at the beach
filled with bits of chaff that scratch at your hand
one nail to hold things together, always out of your grasp

how you spent long nights in shattered sleep
too tired to watch that primetime show that made you snort in laughter
while unconscious arms twitched reflexively
hammering fantasy nails ten feet high
a harmless strike against cotton and feather

how you spent two weeks on your knees with the heavy weight
of a very pregnant belly making you rethink your life choices
or at least the slate tile, pressed by hand into grout
before calling your husband to help you stand
quiet collusion of fetus and gravity too much to bear, on your own

how you will spend the remaining decades of life
explaining to those who can't know
that your diminutive body is stronger
infinitely tougher than they think
as they offer to carry that box or that bag or your load

You can tell from the way their eyes faintly widen
lips parting slightly, a small moue of wonder
that this and that you are not what they expected
that your delicate box has surprised their hands
with its weight.

Bruce Gunther
THE SILENCES

You in your chair,
studying a science video
while looking, as always,
for new ways to enlighten your third-graders.
Me, in a matching recliner
at the other end of the room,
scribbling a few lines,
thinking about love
and its perfectly-normal
Silences.

Outside a pair
of mating cardinals share a space
on the neighbor's forest green
chain-link fence—

They leave together,
relocate on the branch of a pine tree,
which drops its needles without a sound.

Michael Brosnan
SPRINGSTEEN

Lounging on a downpour day,
you listen to the rain drumming on the roof,
spattering off the leaves and flowers. Rain
draining down the spout, soaking the ground soft.
The dampness sloppily peeling back the day's heat.

Curled on the couch, you look up from the book
you are reading—about Bruce Springsteen.
The road, the friction, the music, the story.
He believed in what he wanted and won big.
You stare at the wet window, pat the lazing dog,
which groans and rolls on its back.

That's it. That's all of it. Another moment
lingering with the slow spin of Earth.
But, of course, everything has changed.
And when you get up to pee, you wonder why,
with all of the brain's synaptic firing,
you hadn't fought harder for yourself
in the drawn-out drama of those early days.
The question impossible to answer now without
the steady interruption of shrugs and tears.

You try listening harder to the rain,
how it speaks and doesn't speak your name.

Maggie Walcott
HAMMER AND NAIL

We built this house like they built this city
on rock and roll and love and sweat
on tears from cut skin which danced midair
with small puffy clouds of concrete mix
to dry gray tracks upon our frames, the harmony
of well-placed hammer and profanity keeping our step.

At night we collapsed into each other
plumbing the depths of still hard bodies
like magnets turned north to south
endlessly attracted, even in sleep
sinewy skin and callused hands entwined.

Time checks boxes
like wainscoting and wallpaper
filled wombs and wrinkles
our pride, like our backs, bent
maybe broken, or only inflamed
just never quite the same.

Last night I grasped for your hand in the dark,
seeking its solace through a tangle of sheets
all coiled, crumpled, a labyrinth of cotton
with dead ends infinite, often indifferent
but not necessarily discontent.

The house is long built but I laid a new path,
paving my way against 400-count apathy
until I held the prize of your hand in mine
surprised by its presence, but not like you think
it belongs here still, even if the measurements have changed.
We last took them long ago.

We used to say measure twice, cut thrice
and you bought me a tapeline coiled tightly with fractions,
more nails than needed, a book on timber framing.
We needed the guidance to make our house sound
but glue will hold in a pinch.

Grace McGovern
MIRROR

after Edward Hopper's "New York Interior"

She slumps in tulle,
more cloud than girl.

Hair parts at the nape,
points us down
to the kiss
of shoulder blades.

They are the sharpest things
here

or is it

her hand?

It is more rope
than skin, comes to a point
of flesh and I
can hear the desperate
pulse.

...

Is she hungry?

She looks so hungry.

I imagine her fingers
digging into
her stomach
and I touch my fat
just the same

tilt my head
just the same
droop as she does–
flower without rain.

I eat sleep for breakfast lunch and dinner.
I know she does the same.

Seth Jani
BARN SONG

I'm not sure I could ever come
to the valley or the grave
without first touching
the green, acquitting light,
the dark shine of summer.
It's in my bones, thatched
out of sorrow, out of dawn break,
out of too many winters
taken to the chin.
In my heart too,
which just last evening
was a red bird calling
from the conflagration,
from the burning house
which my father set ablaze
singing *mercy, mercy,*
there's no wind.

Aiden Heung
CHANSON

If I tell you what I know
about the ocean, about the forest, about
the resilient earth that broods
germination;
If I tell you his eyes, his hair,
his lips you'll understand

my metaphor; for I'm the witness
of his every hour of every dawn
of every moon tossing every
tone of lovelornness to this town
of every man but no man
longs for him more

than me; Listen, A thrush
knows it and pricks the crepuscular
landscape he loves with a better
note; I can only reach to the sky

for the flames.

Jeffrey Alfier
CZĘSTOCHOWA SUMMER SUNDAY

Two Cats Café. Black bread and tea, enough to greet
    the warming hour, the storm edging a mottled sky
    breaking to a rinsed-out blue.
A man at a rear table leans on his elbows,
    face in his palms, steam rising from a refilled cup
to his closed eyes. A mother and young son
    hold a tiny banquet of over-rich tarts,
    their morning pared to simplicity. On the patio,
shreds of low voices like an out-of-tune radio,
    patrons in leather jackets favored by cops and thieves.

~*~

I pay up, cut through the shadow of an aged walker,
    one hand on his cane, the other gripping windowsills
    between pots of dead plants, balconies above so close
that ivy reaches from one to another.
    Mannerly trees trick our parks into symmetry.
    I quicken past a beggar's palm, fake a search for coins
    in my pocket. A nun's glare drills me cold.
    The night will fall late, humid hours without a breeze,
window fans on overdrive. Lovers will sprawl on beds,
    uncovered arms opened wide, like falling bodies.

Seth Jani
BREAD

I opened doors because I was obsessed
with the light beyond them,
though no one else shared my happiness
when dragonflies filled the hall.
The windows were shut, and the book
of fables burned for kindling.
I planted small moons in the sky outside,
preparing for famine,
for the hunger to be born.
It didn't matter that the streets
were covered in darkness,
or that the people only believed
in nameable weathers.
Flowers fell and ignited the pavement.
June came and went
with its sacraments of rain.

Joe Cottonwood
BECAUSE LOVE, BECAUSE STUBBORN

One sapling seeks east light.
One, west.
Side by side girths expand, touch, meld.
Two trunks of one mighty tree
rise united at the base
sharing nourishment, support.

I've harvested such pairs.
Milled for lumber
where they join is the prettiest grain,
richest in detail:
whorls, bends, compromises
unstable at the joint.

So, child,
your grandmother a schoolteacher
strict as a rod, pretty as a dandelion;
your grandfather a woodsman
who danced, who brewed his own whiskey,
who could make her laugh or break her bones.

You ask, child,
about your mother, their daughter—
her temper, her beauty, her fragile grain.
Have I explained?

Ellen Stone
DARK CLOUDS

1.

When dark clouds were overhead,
our mother herded us inside.

All the while gloom gathered in her,
stuck there like dirty wool on a sheep

darkening with the days, as if twilight
was always lingering, boiling.

2.

The lake ripples this morning,
rolling sheet on the clothesline.

It's calm, temporary. The sky stews,
giant felt swath sweltering

until the maelstrom hits, pelting us.
Then, the world is a muddled jumble.

3.

Our father used to thrill when storms
blew in – havoc could be kept outside.

He loved the getting ready, battened
down the house, brought wood inside.

The dark clouds inside our mother
never blew over and left, until she did.

4.

The lake is deep and keeps her secrets.
She is the largest mirror we can hold –

so we can see the dark clouds,
at least until the night comes.

At least until we know what deep
fog/front we'll still be living under.

Michael Brosnan

I CAN SEE THE FOG OF HER BREATH

Years ago, we had room to stroll, mull things over.
Here, leisurely there. People met your gaze.
Now we find ourselves turned back constantly,
wall to wall to window to wall. One wall is tagged:
Rare rescue. Another bleeds the faint blue light
of TV's shackling draw. Over here in the corner: snow
and puddles of melted snow—the dissipating remains
of some sense that we really must belong to nature.
Stardust to something to us to (you know, eventually)
another ganglion of will. Life pushing, on and through.
I got down on my knees this morning and kissed the floor.
I got down on my knees and prayed for answers
to two big questions, finding only a dusty, crumpled list
of the musical hits of 1972, written who knows when
and under what influence. These songs hint at an oversoul,
but whirl now with ghost hope, crackling with chords
of old transience. At the one small window:
Pagan deities press their faces to the smudged glass,
squinting as if needing to figure out what has left us
and what can be saved. One of them—Sjöfn, I think—
is yelling through the glass. I can see the fog
of her breath. What I hear is muffled, but sounds like:
Try making something out of not knowing enough.

Jimmy Hollenbeck

FROM HERE WE HUM TOGETHER

after Jamaal May, for Ashley

now look for me, your wood-grain home,

for a tune older than bristlecone pine,

silent as some broken thrum

left to winter and linger

in the feathers of your wing. Flutter

here in the trunk of my wooden chest,

like the shorebird you are,

swollen and swallow, hollow, left

singing until night turns blue. Nest

in my leafless branches,

in my jagged crown,

the timber of my throat.

and when you fly

and warble, I'll lumber you

south, keep my dirt-drenched roots

and stumble, these fallen branches

for company. Whistle in your sway,

the wind for your flight. I'll hear your

twitter and sing

soft songbird chitter,

the rhythm of your puffed chest,

and whistle sweetly along

the song of your body. Hummingbird,

knowing I've always wanted

this sugar water for your beak to be

the beat of your wings

left tender and raw,

singing me to sleep.

Blake Lynch
LIGHT

When I was a child, I thought everything
I had to say was important—so I'd wake
and scribble something down
without turning on the light, while outside
the fog had barely begun to catch through
the trees that surrounded our house.

I'd write about how after a girl left you, all that
you could see all night were three crows
settled on the roof of a cottage beginning
to fall apart, until the light came up.

Now, years later, I flip the circuits in my house,
and watch as the form of everything, the chairs,
the table, the windows, dances away for a moment,
as I tighten a headlamp, but then it comes back,
out of nothing, the ability to know exactly where
I am even in the darkness.

I'm old now, and I know exactly when it happened,
a few years ago, when the air was just as cold as it is
this morning, slowly beginning to betray you,
and turn the trees into watchmen overnight.
I was in Jameson Hospital with cancer in my lungs,
not sure if I would last, not sure if death would come
in the night following behind a nurse or cup of bills,
and then Dr Simon came before six o'clock,
the look in her eyes even colder than the winter.

She held my hand, and said:
No, you damn fool, it's not going to kill you.

And the cold came rising off the fields,
and the snow began to fall,

and the whistle of the night train passing
through the south side woke up the whole neighborhood,
before the light came, when we all lay awake
in our beds, like children waiting for something.

Mark Robinson

CONSIDERING WHERE THE DEAD GO

The black leafless trees sit at the edge of your ghost-
stage, and everything smells of rain. In the distance,
clouds gather. Light sky, dark sky
push against each other, trying to reconcile your absence
and for a moment you were nowhere
before soul absorbed by moon.

Where in that blank sky was the moon?
A parcel from Portmagee arrived. Oh, our Irish ghost
saying hello, I told them. Maybe there was nowhere
you couldn't be. Maybe you could travel a great distance
in a moment. Maybe there really was no absence.
Maybe whenever I wanted I could summon from the sky

your presence, your shifting sky
above my shifting ground. The moon
felt your absence though:
for weeks it was a hollow ghost
in the distance,
then it was nowhere.

Is the world filled with heaven? Nowhere
is just a place to disappear for a minute. Distance
doesn't really exist: the space between clouds in the sky,
at my doorstep tonight is the moon.
The black leafless trees sit at the edge of your ghost-
stage and I embrace your absence

in an urgent plea for grace. Absence
that is not a nowhere
but instead a rather ever-present ghost
sensing the sugary sky
the glowing moon
the distance.

Distance,
absence,
moon,
nowhere,
sky,
ghost.

Listen, in the distance, at the edge of nowhere
your absence fills the sky:
my moon-ghost.

CONTRIBUTOR BIOS

RENEE AGATEP writes of her rust belt beginnings in Ohio and now lives in St. Augustine, Florida. Renee earned her master's at Northeastern University and is currently studying creative writing at the University of Central Florida. Her poetry is forthcoming in the *Texas Poetry Calendar.*

JEFFREY ALFIER's most recent book is *The Shadow Field* (Louisiana Literature Press, 2020). He is co-editor of *Blue Horse Press* and *San Pedro River Review.*

SYDNEY BOLLINGER is an Atlanta-based writer with an MS in environmental writing from the University of Montana. Sydney writes about the environment and theology. Her work can be found in *Young Ignorantes, Cultured Vultures, Orris Root,* and other places. Find her online @sydboll.

HAYLEY BOWEN is pursuing her MFA in creative writing at Syracuse University. Born in Southern California, raised in the foothills of Colorado, and a recent graduate of Black Hills State University, Hayley is an obsessive observer of the wondrous world she occupies.

MICHAEL BROSNAN's most recent poetry book is *The Sovereignty of the Accidental* (Harbor Mountain Press, 2019). He's also the author of *Against the Current,* a book on inner-city education, and serves as the editor for the website Teaching While White.

KEVIN CASEY is the author of *Ways to Make a Halo* (Aldrich Press, 2018) and *American Lotus* (Glass Lyre Press, 2018). *And Waking...* was published by Bottom Dog Press in 2016. His poems have appeared in *Rust+Moth, Valparaiso Poetry Review,* and Ted Kooser's syndicated column *American Life in Poetry.*

*PATRICIA CLARK is the author of *The Canopy,* her fifth book of poems, and three chapbooks, including *Deadlift*. She also writes fiction, and her story "Let Him In," won first prize in the adult division and was published in the Write Michigan 2016 Anthology. Her new book of poems (2020) is titled *Self-Portrait with a Million Dollars.*

CATHERINE C. CON grew up in Taiwan. She earned a BA in English Literature from Fu-Jen Catholic University in Taipei and an MS in information systems from Louisiana State University. She teaches computer science at University of South Carolina. Her work appears in *Emrys Journal, Tint Journal,* and others. She was nominated for a 2020 PEN award.

JOE COTTONWOOD has built or repaired hundreds of houses to support his writing habit in the Santa Cruz Mountains of California. His latest book is *Foggy Dog.*

JOE DAVIES's short fiction has appeared in *The Dublin Review, Prism International, Rampike, The Missouri Review, Gordon Square Review, Queen's Quarterly, eFiction India* and a smattering of other magazines and journals. He lives in Peterborough, Ontario.

MARIYA (MASHA) DEYKUTE is a Russian-American poet, translator, and teacher. She teaches rhetoric and creative writing in Kazakhstan and writes about the wilderness alongside and inside all of us. Her writing most recently appeared in *Seventh Wave* magazine, *Incessant Pipe* and *Soundings East.*

LIZZY DREW is a senior at the Orange County School of the Arts. Her work appears in *Aerie International*, and her school's award-winning literary magazine *Inkblot*. She's interested in the dynamics of science and poetry in the body, and complexifying mental illness through language and form.

STUART FORREST was born in Omaha, Nebraska in 1951. He is a retired county employee who developed a passion for creative writing while attending Stanford University Continuing Studies in 2012. He writes poems, short stories, and screenplays and posts them on his website: stuwriteshere.net.

*RANDALL R. FREISINGER's poems have appeared in numerous magazines and anthologies and have been nominated for a Pushcart Prize nine times. His five collections include *Plato's Breath*, winner of the 1997 May Swenson Poetry Prize (Utah State University Press) and *Windthrow & Salvage* (Kelsay Books, 2019). He lives and writes in Michigan's Upper Peninsula.

CARRIE GEORGE is an MFA candidate at the Northeast Ohio MFA program. She is the current graduate fellow for the Wick Poetry Center in Kent, OH, where she teaches poetry in the community. Her work has appeared in *Gordon Square Review, Spectrum Literary Journal* and *Emerson Review.*

*ABIGAIL GOODHART received their MFA at Western Michigan University. They have published poems in *Atlanta Review, Passages North,* and *Sugar House Review.* They draw inspiration from the culture of the Midwest, the absurdism of the web, and the frenzy of playing roller derby.

ROBIN GOW is a trans poet and young adult author. They are the author of *Our Lady of Perpetual Degeneracy* (Tolsun Books, 2020) and the chapbook *Honeysuckle* (Finishing Line Press, 2019). Their first young adult novel, *A Million Quiet Revolutions*, is slated for publication Winter 2022 with FSG.

JEREMY GREGERSEN is a graduate of the Universities of Utah (BA), Michigan (MFA), and Oregon (MA). His work has appeared in *Cimarron Review, Poet Lore, Juked, Cortland Review, The Maine Review*, and *Michigan Quarterly Review*. He lives in Las Vegas, Nevada with his wife and two sons, and works as Head of School at The Meadows School.

*BRUCE GUNTHER is a former journalist, editor, and freelance writer who's now retired and concentrating on personal writing, among other projects. He's a graduate of Central Michigan University who lives in Bay City with his wife, Trish.

*TIM HAWKINS lives near Grand Rapids, Michigan and is the author of Wanderings at Deadline (Aldrich Press, 2012), Jeremiad Johnson (In Case of Emergency Press, 2019), and Synchronized Swimmers (KYSO Flash Press, 2019). Another poetry collection, West of the Backstory, is forthcoming from Fernwood Press in late 2020. More at: www.timhawkinspoetry.com

AIDEN HEUNG was born and raised on the edge of the Tibetan Plateau. He holds an MA in literature from Tongji University in Shanghai. His work appears in *Poet Lore, Hobart, Parentheses, Cha: An Asian Literary Journal*. He was shortlisted for the 2020 Doug Draime Poetry Prize and awarded the 2019 Hong Kong Proverse Poetry Prize.

TODD HELDT is a poet and librarian living in Chicago. His first collection of poetry, *Card Tricks for the Starving,* was published by Ghost Road Press in 2009. He also runs the information literacy website lis101.com.

*A lifelong Michigander, JIMMY HOLLENBECK will be moving to Ohio in the fall to pursue an MFA at Miami University. He currently serves as a fiction editor for *Great Lakes Review*, and his work has been published in *The Central Review, Gyroscope Review*, and *Flash Glass*.

SETH JANI lives in Seattle, Washington. Their work has appeared in *The American Poetry Journal, Chiron Review, Ghost City Review, Rust+Moth* and Pretty *Owl Poetry,* among others. Their full-length collection, *Night Fable,* was published by FutureCycle Press in 2018. Visit them at www.sethjani.com.

BETSY JOHNSON's work has appeared in *The Iowa Review* (online), *Boulevard, Prairie Schooner, Alaska Quarterly Review, Commonweal,* and *Hayden's Ferry Review*. She lives in Minnesota.

CHRIS KETCHUM is from northern Idaho. He is an MFA candidate at Vanderbilt University, and poetry editor for *Nashville Review*. His poems have appeared or are forthcoming in *Five Points, The Pinch,* and *Tar River Poetry.*

PAUL LUIKART is the author of the short story collections *Animal Heart* (Hyperborea Publishing, 2016) and *Brief Instructions* (Ghostbird Press, 2017). He is adjunct professor of fiction writing at Covenant College in Lookout Mountain, Georgia. He and his family live in Chattanooga, Tennessee.

BLAKE LYNCH is a law school graduate, media journalist, and late stage cancer survivor whose poems have appeared in *Southampton Review, Pulp Magazine, Turk's Head Review*, and *Chelsea* among others. He has also appeared in *Rolling Stone.*

GRACE MCGOVERN is a writer from Chicago with a love of flowers, tea, and flowery tea. Grace's work has appeared in *River River, Open Minds Quarterly,* and *Inklette,* and she was the recipient of the 2016 and 2018 Academy of American Poet's University Prize.

MICHAEL MARK's poetry has been published or is forthcoming in *Copper Nickel, Dunes Review, Michigan Quarterly Review, Salamander, The Southern Review, The New York Times, The Sun, Waxwing, The Poetry Foundation's American Life in Poetry,* and *Verse Daily.* www.michaeljmark.com

A librarian brought up among musicians, *NICCO PANDOLFI lives in Lake Leelanau, MI, where he and his wife are raising a cat and a garden. His poetry, reviews, and nonfiction have appeared in *Dunes Review, Pulp,* and *Edible Grande Traverse.*

Born and raised in the Pacific Northwest, TRISTAN RIVERS uses direct experience with landscapes to explore a unifying experiential essence which is often lost in the distractions of twenty-first century life. He works as a backcountry ranger for the US Forest Service at Mount St. Helens in Washington.

MARK ROBINSON is the author of *Just Last Days* (2020) and an MFA candidate at Lindenwood University. His work appears in *Levee Magazine, Naugatuck River Review, Bending Genres, Gyroscope Review,* and Red Flag Poetry postcard series. Mark lives in Des Moines, his hometown, with his wife Jen and their children Lyla, Aya, Liam, Cora and Minni.

*LISA SCHULTE is a West Indian artist living in Traverse City. She has studied opera in England, graphic design and culinary at NMC in Traverse City, and sailed across the Atlantic in a 37-foot sailboat. She assists in the Culinary Arts program at the TBAISD Career-Tech Center.

*NANCY SQUIRES is the author of a self-published memoir, *The Cottage: Portrait of a Place,* and her work has previously appeared in Dunes Review. She lives in Michigan with her partner and two cats.

*PHILLIP STERLING's most recent collection of poems is *Short on Days* (Main Street Rag, 2020).

*ELLEN STONE considers rural northeastern Pennsylvania, Ann Arbor, and up north Michigan home. She is the author of *What Is in the Blood* (Mayapple Press, 2020) and *The Solid Living World* (Michigan Writers' Cooperative Press, 2013). Ellen's poetry has been nominated for the Pushcart prize and Best of the Net. ellenstone.org

*MAGGIE WALCOTT lives in the Michigan wilderness with her high school sweetheart and their two children, in a house they built themselves. Her nonfiction piece "An Open Vessel," was published by *Mothers Always Write* in 2019 and will be republished by *Uncomfortable Revolution* in 2020.

READER BIOS

*PETER BOISVERT is a native Detroiter who now lives, works, and writes in Ann Arbor. He pays the bills writing code, writes poems and stories in between, is a fairly recent graduate of Pacific University's MFA program, still prefers to sit in the dark in an actual movie theater and cry when the hero comes back for the kid, and one year inspected and certified all the rubber life rafts carried on the sailboats running in the Port Huron to Mackinaw race.

*MELISSA FOURNIER lives and works in Traverse City, Michigan. Her work has appeared in *Dunes Review, The Sow's Ear Poetry Review, Pulse: Voices from the Heart of Medicine*, and Medical Literary Messenger. Melissa is co-editor of the anthology *AFTER, Stories about Loss and What Comes Next* (Barnwood Books) and is author of the chapbook, *Abruptio* (The Poetry Box). She has a background in mental health, adult, pediatric and perinatal hospice.

*LUJINE NASRALLA is managing editor of *Dunes Review* and serves as a board member of Michigan Writers. A Communications Specialist at ACCESS, a community nonproft, she spends most of her time writing, reading, or doing something outside. Born and raised in East Dearborn, she currently lives in Detroit.

*TERESA SCOLLON is the author of the poetry collection *To Embroider the Ground with Prayer* (Wayne State University Press). Her essay was included in *Elemental*, an anthology of Michigan essayists. She is a National Endowment for the Arts fellow and won the 2018 Moveen Poetry Prize. She teaches the Front Street Writers program at the TBAISD Career-Tech Center.

*When EMMA SMITH was in middle school, teachers said she was having difficulty reading. As her worried parents contemplated purchasing Hooked on Phonics, Emma picked up *IT* by Stephen King and hasn't slowed down since. She loves to read everything from sci fi/fantasy to oudated anarchist literature to the classics. You can find Emma working with animals, reading books, or hiking with friends.

*JENNIFER YEATTS' literary life has included MA and MFA degrees in poetry, teaching writing in various forms, and editorial roles at *Passages North* and *Fugue*. She is director of coffee for Higher Grounds Trading Company.

*denotes Michigan native or resident

SUBMISSION GUIDELINES

Dunes Review welcomes work from writers, artists, and photographers at all stages of their careers living anywhere in the world, though we particularly love featuring writers with ties to Michigan and the Midwest. We are open to all styles and aesthetics, but please read the following paragraph carefully to dive a little deeper into what we're looking for.

Ultimately, we're looking for work that draws us in from the very first line: with image, with sound, with sense, with lack of sense. We're looking for writing that makes us *feel* and bowls us over, lifts us up, and takes us places we've never been to show us ordinary things in ways we've never seen them. We're looking for poems and stories and essays that teach us how to read them and pull us back to their beginnings as soon as we've read their final lines. We're looking for things we can't wait to read again, things we can't wait to share with the nearest person who will listen. Send us your best work. We'll give it our best attention.

Submissions are accepted only via our Submittable platform: dunesreview.submittable.com. We do not consider work sent through postal mail or email. Any submissions sent through email will not be read or responded to. Please see further guidelines posted on our site. We look forward to reading your work!

Call for Patrons

Dunes Review is a not-for-profit endeavor to promote creative work within the Northern Michigan writing community and beyond.

The cost of publication can be underwritten in part by individual contributions. We invite you to support the publication of the next issue with a donation of $25.

Send your check payable to **Michigan Writers** to:

Michigan Writers
P.O. Box 2355
Traverse City, MI 49685

Thank you in advance for your support!

Michigan
WRITERS

Michigan Writers
P.O. Box 2355
Traverse City, Michigan 49685
dunesreview@michwriters.org

Made in the USA
Monee, IL
27 August 2020